AMAZING ANIMAL TALES

Little Tiger

Can you spot the line of marching ants on every page?

AMAZING ANIMAL TALES

Little Tiger

ANNE ROONEY   CAROLINA RABEI

OXFORD
UNIVERSITY PRESS

Deep in the rainforest, Little Tiger lies hidden in his cosy den. Outside, the rain plops heavily from the leaves and the sun rises above the treetops.

Inside, Mamma tiger curls around her babies. The cubs are safe and snug. A soothing smell of wet earth and warm bodies fills the den.

AMAZING ANIMAL TALES

Little Tiger

ANNE ROONEY   CAROLINA RABEI

OXFORD
UNIVERSITY PRESS

Deep in the rainforest, Little Tiger lies hidden in his cosy den. Outside, the rain plops heavily from the leaves and the sun rises above the treetops.

Inside, Mamma tiger curls around her babies. The cubs are safe and snug. A soothing smell of wet earth and warm bodies fills the den.

Drip,
drip,
drip, drop!

A newborn cub is as heavy as a bag of sugar.

1kg Sugar

Many tigers live in the tropical rainforests of Asia. It's very hot and wet.

The mother tiger finds a secret den to give birth to her cubs. She usually has two or three cubs.

Can you spot three hidden dens?

The cubs drink sweet, warm milk and doze happily. Little Tiger shuffles and snuffles, milk trickling into his fur.

His sister pushes him with the soft pads of her paws. She wants the best spot against Mamma's furry tummy, but he hasn't finished yet! He grumbles and wriggles closer.

Creeping outside, Little Tiger blinks in the sunlight. Howling monkeys and squawking birds call from the treetops.

His paws sink deep into the leaves.

He jumps as something squirms over his toes!

Mamma watches her cubs bite and fight with their sharp new teeth and claws.

It's only play,
and no one is hurt.

Cubs start to explore outside after eight weeks. They play fight, getting ready for life as fierce hunters!

Tiger cubs are born with their eyes closed. They open them around ten days later.

Their eyes are blue when they open.

At around four months old, they change to gold.

Little Tiger scratches his claws against a tree. They snag in the bark. Could he climb up?

Suddenly, crashes rumble through the forest.

CRASH
CRASH
CRASH!
What's that?

Little Tiger scrambles up, away from the scary noise.

But, oh dear, it's a long way down! Little Tiger cries for Mamma. She peers up into the branches.

Little Tiger scrabbles desperately as Mamma climbs.

His paws ache and he can't hold on much longer.

At last, she reaches him! Mamma carries a tired Little Tiger back to the den, gripping his fur gently in her teeth. Her warm breath on his neck chases away his fears.

Big tigers don't drink milk. Soon, Little Tiger will need to catch his own food, so Mamma Tiger teaches her cubs to hunt.

First, crouch . . .

. . . then creep and . . .

POUNCE!

A snake! Little Tiger leaps away as it strikes.

Poor Little Tiger bounds over to
Mamma and she licks his head.

Baby tigers are born without teeth — just like you! When their milk teeth grow, they practise biting.

Larger, stronger teeth grow before the cub is a year old. A grown-up tiger has 30 teeth.

It uses them to hunt large animals to eat.

Measure your hand against an adult tiger's tooth.

20
19
18
17
16
15
14
13
12
11
10
9
8
7
6
5
4
3
2
1
0 cm

The cubs play and scamper through the leaves on their way home. Little Tiger rolls like a ball down the soft slope.

Uh-oh! What's happening?

He tumbles faster and faster! His sisters try to keep up, their paws skidding and slipping on the ground. But —

SPLASH!

The water feels lovely and cool.
Little Tiger's paws move him easily
through the pool.

He swishes his tail
happily, making ripples.

But wait, something is nibbling him! He jumps onto the bank, scattering water everywhere!

Back in their cosy den, Mamma licks the cubs clean and dry. Her warm tongue is soothing.

Little Tiger feels safe and loved.

With tummies full of fish,
the cubs curl up together.
Little Tiger yawns and snuggles
deeper into his mamma's fur.
Goodnight, Little Tiger!

A grown tiger's tail is a metre long.
Are you as tall as a tiger's tail?

Each tiger has its own pattern of stripes that helps it hide in the forest. Cubs look stripier than grown-ups as the stripes are all crowded together on a small body!

OXFORD
UNIVERSITY PRESS

Great Clarendon Street, Oxford OX2 6DP

Oxford University Press is a department of the University of Oxford.
It furthers the University's objective of excellence in research, scholarship,
and education by publishing worldwide. Oxford is a registered trade mark
of Oxford University Press in the UK and in certain other countries

Database right Oxford University Press (maker)

First published in 2022

British Library Cataloguing in Publication Data

Data available

ISBN: 978-0-19-278097-3

1 3 5 7 9 10 8 6 4 2

Printed in China

Paper used in the production of this book is a natural,
recyclable product made from wood grown in sustainable forests.
The manufacturing process conforms to the environmental
regulations of the country of origin.